Carlito's World

A Block in Spanish Harlem

by Veronica Nash

illustrated by David K. Stone

Carlito's World: A Block in Spanish Harlem may be read independently by upper second level readers. The high interest basis makes it appealing to those reading beginning second level as well as to readers normally able to cope with more difficult materials.

Carlito's World: A Block in Spanish Harlem was classroom tested and the Spache Readability Formula was applied. We thank Mrs. June Stern, Reading Consultant in the Commack Public Schools, Commack, Long Island, New York, for this help.

H. Alan Robinson, Professor of Reading
Hofstra University, Old Westbury, N.Y.

A Rutledge Book

Copyright © 1969 by McGraw-Hill, Inc.
All rights reserved
Library of Congress Catalog Card Number 78-77094
Printed in the United States of America

McGraw-Hill Book Company
New York/Toronto/London/Sydney

My name is Carlos but everyone calls me Carlito. Carlito means little Carlos in Spanish.

I live up this block in the city of New York. Almost everyone who lives here is Puerto Rican. There are many apartment houses here. Many families live in each one of them.

When my parents came from Puerto Rico to live in New York, they came to this block. My Aunt Rosa already lived here. She found an apartment for us.

Our apartment is on the second floor. My friend Pablo lives on the sixth floor. My mother leans out our window to call me when dinner is ready.

Our apartment is long and narrow. It has three rooms. All the rooms are small except the kitchen. It has a big round table in it where we eat. My sister Elena and I do our homework on this table. Sometimes my mother sits with us and sews.

At home we often speak Spanish. It is the language my parents spoke in Puerto Rico, before they moved to New York.

We have five people in our family so our apartment is crowded.

I share a bedroom with my brother Juan who is sixteen. He works after school at the supermarket. Juan also plays the guitar. Sometimes he tries to teach me to play.

At night I like to sit at our window and look down on the street. I can see Juan and his friends sitting on the steps. They listen to their radios and talk.

There is always traffic on our street. When we play we have to watch out for the cars.

There is a fire here almost every day. Fire engines speed down the street ringing their bells and sirens. Sometimes we run to see where the fire is.

The gray smoke fills up the sky. Some people from the building on fire come down the fire escape. Others wait for the firemen to help them get out.

Our street is very dirty. The garbage cans get too
full. They spill out onto the sidewalks and streets.
There is broken glass on the street, too.

On this block there is an empty lot. It is full of
broken furniture and other things people throw away.

I walk to the public school three blocks away. A policewoman helps us cross the wide, busy avenue.

All the windows at our school have wire screens over them so no one can break the glass.

Our teacher is young and hardly ever gets angry with us. Our class is big, but I know everyone's name.

On special days our class takes trips to learn different things. My favorite was the Museum of Natural History. A man there showed us animals I had never seen before.

After school we play handball against the sides of the
buildings. Other times we walk to the park to play stickball.
In the summer a policeman comes to turn on the fire

hydrant. Water shoots out into the street for us to play in. Kids come from all over. Some wear bathing suits. Some run through the water with their clothes on.

We make up new games, too. The workmen who dig up the streets sometimes leave giant round spools of wire. We try to push them and climb to the top.

The people in the park gave us some lumber and nails to build things. It was fun to break up what we built and then build something new.

We climb up the wire fence in the ball park. It is as high as the trees.

There are kids here who like to fight. They yell at me and my friends. We get angry and fight them back. I don't like to fight but sometimes I have to.

The worst thing is when the kids start to throw bottles. The glass crashes on the sidewalk, everyone ducks and runs.

All the walls in our neighborhood have writing on them. People like to write their names. Some draw pictures.

There are posters on the walls, too. I like to look at the pictures on them. When we get a box of chalk we draw on the sidewalk.

There are some bad people here who steal from apartments and stores. At night all the stores have iron gates across the front so no one can get in.

Many people have big dogs to guard their apartments. Our dog is named *Toro*, which means "bull" in Spanish. My father says he is as strong as a bull. *Toro* barks loudly when anyone comes to our door.

I like to go shopping with my mother. She lets me pull the cart we use to carry everything home in.

We go to the grocery where the man speaks Spanish with my mother. She buys rice and *chorizos,* which are sausages. We pick out fruit and vegetables at the stands on the street.

Then my mother gives me pennies for the gum machines by the candy store.

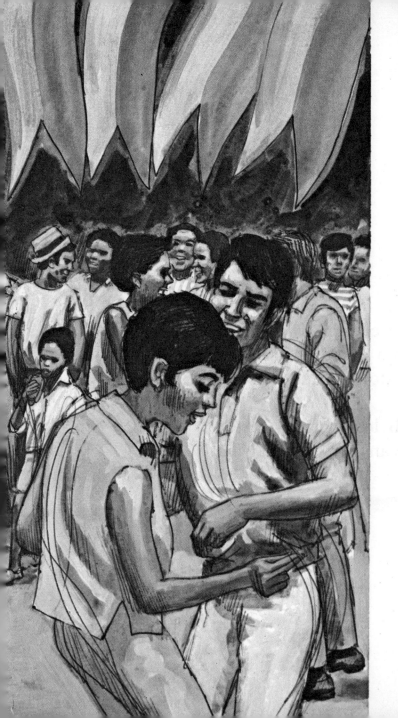

Last summer we had an out-door party on our block. All the families who live on our street came.

There were orange and yellow flags that made the street look pretty. We had hot dogs and cold cans of soda.

The policeman closed off our street so we could play with no traffic. There was music all day from guitars and bongo drums.

Our street was filled with noise. Good noise. From singing and talking and laughing.

Sometimes on Sunday, after church, we go to visit my aunt. She lives far away in a different part of the city called the Bronx. We have to take the subway to get there.

The trains go fast through long, dark tunnels. I like to ride in the first car. I can look out and make believe I am driving the train.

I like my neighborhood. There are always things to do and friends to play with. But I want to see other places, too.

Someday, if my father gets a car, he can take me to the country. I want to see a live snake and catch a fish and maybe even ride a horse.

ABOUT THE AUTHOR

Veronica Nash was born in New York City and worked as a fashion copywriter in a Boston ad agency, where she met her husband, an illustrator. For a while, Veronica Nash lived in New York's East Village, but presently she lives with her husband in Boston. While in New York, she was an artist's agent whose clients included her husband, now a successful book illustrator. This is the author's first book.

ABOUT THE ARTIST

David Stone received a B.A. degree from the University of Oregon. He also did graduate work at Oregon as well as at the Art Center at Los Angeles and the Universidad de Michoacan, Mexico. In 1968 he was elected President of the Society of Illustrators in New York. He also organized the annual National Exhibition of Illustration. Mr. Stone has illustrated many juveniles and textbooks.